DILLIE KEAN

The Joy of Sequins

THE
FASCINATING AÏDA
SONGBOOK

METHUEN

First published in Great Britain in 1994 by Methuen London
an imprint of Reed Consumer Books Ltd
Michelin House, 81 Fulham Road, London SW3 6RB
and Auckland, Melbourne, Singapore and Toronto
Copyright in the compilation and introductions © 1994 by Dillie Keane
The author has asserted her moral rights
Text and music copyright © as indicated in individual songs
Performance photographs copyright © 1994 by Simon Annand
Studio photographs copyright © 1994 by Johnny Boylan

A CIP catalogue record for this book is available at the British Library
ISBN 0 413 69110 1

Designed by Katy Hepburn
Text typeset by Falcon Graphic Art
Music set by Seton Music Graphics Ltd,
Bantry, Co Cork, Ireland
Printed and bound in Great Britain
by Clays Ltd, St Ives plc

CONTENTS

These photos are not really representative, as they don't show the flowers, champagne and gifts of jewellery from diminutive exiled princes, or the throngs of stage-door johnnies that usually hang about, hoping for a kind word and an agreement to go to supper at the Café Royal.

ALL THAT GLITTER!

I wrote my first song when I was eleven. My mother had bought me my first real, fab gear, grown-up dress. It was a Dollyrocker: red and blue check, six inches above the knee. I thought I was the coolest chick in town, and I wrote a song about it immediately. It went:

> Woo baby – woo-oo-oo
> Woo-baby – woo-oo-oo
> Woo-baby – woo-oo-oo

Gonna wear my Dollyrocker, yeah, storm the town.

It was a great hit with the family, who asked me to sing it on any and every occasion, even waking me up at three in the morning to come down in my jim-jams and entertain whoever wasn't under the sofa by that time. The family had been hoping to produce a genius ever since my mother had her tonsils removed by Oliver St John Gogarty, writer, friend of James Joyce and renowned tonsil thief. The sudden proximity to the world of letters raised their hopes, and so a genius was sought. Sadly for my family, who are perfectly good people in every way and deserve a great deal better, the nearest thing to an artistic genius was me. But bless their cotton socks, they hailed my Dollyrocker song as a sign of impending greatness. My father saw the Albert Hall beckoning.

Flushed with success, I took up the guitar, went on writing songs and developed a temperament to go with my new-found creativity. I was soon refusing to sing my Dollyrocker number (or any other old material for that matter), wishing only to focus on new work, in the manner of creative artistes and other wankers the world over. I had also taken to making my own clothes in needlework classes, which may explain the absence of any more garment-inspired numbers. Added to which, 'Bell-bottoms' does not have the same scannable euphony as the word 'Dollyrocker'.

Much influenced by surrealism and psychedelia, I wrote some quirky ditties – 'Dream', a huge favourite with the Lower Fifth at the Sacred Heart Convent, and 'Swingin' Little Muddletown on the Puddlemarsh', my first comedy number. Both scored huge votes at the school pop concert, though not enough to gain the coveted Number One Spot, which was taken by a stonkingly good song called 'Robots', penned by my classmates Green and Inky.

The blow was bitter. I don't see either Green or Inky any more.

Anyhow, 'Swingin' Little Muddletown on the Puddlemarsh' is a stinker. It is a dead rat on the compost heap of life. My brother always asks to hear it when the spirit of fraternal meanness overcomes him and he feels like having a snigger. On such occasions, if he weren't bigger and stronger than me, I'd sock him in the kisser. It's a relief he can't remember all the dreary adolescent songs about depression and death that I went on to write.

For various reasons I gradually stopped writing. Adolescent obsession with depression and death, for starters. Then Frances Hunter-Gordon, founder president of the school Pop Club and Wine-Making Society, wrote a guitar Mass, which was recorded by the school choir at the very EMI studios in St John's Wood where the Beatles had recorded *Abbey Road*. Crikey! What a day that was!

We went up to London in a coach accompanied by a handful of nuns and, on arrival at the studios, kept a febrile and vigilant eye out for any Beatles that might be lurking in the building. We assumed that they went to work there every day. The stakes were raised considerably when someone said that George Martin was in the control room. He was a disappointing-looking short bloke, weedy even, with ginger hair, freckles and glasses. (Years later, I saw George Martin in the flesh, and he had changed considerably, becoming a tall, well built, imposing and distinguished man with excellent sight and no trace of red hair or freckles. It's amazing how success can change a person.)

The day continued miraculous; we bought pasties from a very advanced sort of vending machine, and had them heated up in a matter of seconds in an astounding thing called a microwave. We sat in a sort of sitting room, gossiping about the sound men, and how we could get them to fancy us. In studio, we rolled up our skirts around our waists, and pretended (a) not to be wearing uniform, and (b) not to know who the nuns were. We longed for a sound man, George Martin even, to hurl us up against a wall and tell us he couldn't live without us.

So Frances Hunter-Gordon's Mass was duly recorded. It's the last (and only) album to feature me as a guitarist. I listen to it now and again and, though I laugh at our youthful, upper-class girlish voices, our syncopation-free strumming and our four-square beat, I am still touched by the sweet simplicity of her music and settings. She had great talent, and it's a shame that she has entirely given up her music these days.

So then I grew despondent, haunted by the knowledge that I could never scale such heights. Even Green and Inky stopped writing in the teeth of Frances Hunter-Gordon's brilliance.

Then one day someone played me a record by Tom Lehrer, called *That Was The Year That Was*. It featured, amongst others, 'The Vatican Rag', and it seemed like he sang with my secret inner voice, and thus there was no point in trying to compete. And besides, I was going to be an Actress. Not a Pianist.

ME AND THE PIANO

Everyone envies a pianist. You're at a party, and there's a piano. 'Hoorah,' says someone loudly, 'here's a gal who can tickle the ovaries.' (Me.)

So after a lot of public persuasion and private demurring, you sit down smiling, with an inner scowl, and hack out a few tunes. Two drunks sing along, three people look at you and wish they had taken their Grade Eight. The rest of the guests continue chatting loudly about the age of consent, women priests, or whatever the current topic of debate happens to be.

Then someone else comes up and insists you sing 'I Fancy the Pope' (a still-amusing song I penned way back in 1985). Everyone joins in the clamour for their Favourite Comedic Numero in the History of the Universe, even though only one person in the room has heard it. You finally agree, by which time everyone has heard the punch-line, 'I Fancy the Pope' (which is why the song's actual title is 'My Dream Man'), and the comic effect is killed. The idea of Fancying the Pope must be a surprise, or all is lost. By the time you get halfway through the first chorus, they're all back to chatting about the ERM.

Then as you sing your finest comic number to a darkened room full of people who are, at best, vaguely amused, the man of your dreams enters. You have fancied him for months; he has taken you out for dinner a couple of times and things are progressing nicely. He sees you singing 'I Fancy the Pope' to three bearded stalwarts in kagoules. All the people in hip Paul Smith suits are chatting up the leggy redheads. He clocks you sitting there at the keyboard, pretending to be Fats Waller, but with less sex appeal, and owning up to a penchant for the World's Number One Vicar. He heads for the nearest redhead.

That's the minus side of being able to play the piano at parties.

The advantage is that it saves having to flirt.

The piano has been my torment and joy always. I was playing by ear at three, but for some reason I'm barely competent technically. It grieves me that I will never have the skill to be anything better than a decent enough hack. My laziness is

Everyone goes head over heels for a piano.

only slightly to blame – the gift is simply not mine. Yet it obsesses me. While others grooved at the Isle of Wight and familiarised themselves with the lesser-known riffs of Buddy Guy, I slaved as a teenager at my Chopin and Beethoven. For all that, the only thing I really had a gift for playing was ragtime.

I rarely play anything without several mistakes, nor can I play anything the same way twice. I do think with my hands, however, not with my mind, and this applies to the typewriter keyboard as well; I can't write prose with a pen, and never could. I really know my way around the keyboard, and can play without looking at the keys. In fact, I play better if I don't look at the keys. This is probably because, as a child, I practised in the dark with my eyes closed – just in case I went blind later, and had to earn my living as a pianist. I was a melodramatic little girl.

To play solo makes me sob with fright. I play a piano solo in 'Blues got a Skeleton Key'. It was only inserted at Adèle's insistence, and I dread it every night. All the same, I know I have a good touch, and to accompany a gifted singer competently is the most extraordinary pleasure. I couldn't bear to play at all after Fascinating Aïda disbanded in 1989, though I'm loving playing again now, probably because I have given up hope of ever being really good, and am relaxing about it for the first time in my life.

The piano is a thorn in my flesh, and yet it's the first thing I turn to when I'm distressed. I hate it, and I can't live without it.

ME AND THE ALBERT HALL

I eventually got to play the Albert Hall. Actually, it was called Albert's Hall. It is/was a bar in Stockholm. I had the most awful time. My father refused to be impressed.

WRITING

Real songs started to arrive at the song terminus in my brain in 1981. In 1983, I set out on the thorny path of collaboration with my old friend Marilyn Cutts, co-founder of Fascinating Aïda. I firmly believe that in a group of three people, having only one – or even two – writers is divisive. The songs end up being the richer for being subjected to team scrutiny and for being the sum of three people's experiences.

That said, finding Adèle Anderson was like finding the other half of the sixpence. We were born three weeks and twenty miles apart, and in some ways we're symbiotic. We have been collaborating continuously ever since we met in 1984. She says I'm the architect, and she's the bricklayer, a very good description of the way we work.

Generally, I think up the ideas, sketch out a rough shape, play and hum a wobbly sort of tune, and somehow, she divines my idea, and we start work. It's a ghastly process, not least because we have completely different ways of working. We're like an interchangeable tortoise and hare. Adèle is a real stickler for grammar, which drives me gaga because she jams up the works with her literalism, whereas I am a real botch-job merchant, which has her grinding her teeth in frustration. I, however, will go back once a song is apparently complete, and twiddle with it forever – it's never finished as far as I'm concerned. Adèle, on the other hand, likes to set it in stone once it's reached performance level.

If I should lose confidence in an idea, I get a black cloud of Irish gloom around my head, and jettison whatever work we've done. It's now a recognised sign that if I go off and do some gardening when we're supposed to be working, things are going badly. Adèle sits at the table, disciplined to the last, and will peg on steadily until it's complete. On the other hand, she always likes to finish a song in a day, and gets despondent if she doesn't. Then it's my turn to be tortoise, because I am quite content to take forever – it's not unusual for a song to take eighteen months.

We are hugely grateful to the wine-makers of Australia, since were it not for the healing properties in a bottle of Coonawarra Chardonnay, many a song might not have been written, and many steaks would have been purchased (to put on the black eyes we'd have given one another).

Many people have tried to downplay Adèle's contribution to the songs. Quite simply, I will not have it. In the beginning, when I first discovered that I could write songs, they slipped out fully formed, one on top of the other, faster than I could believe. Now I find them terribly hard to write. The ideas arrive, and then elude me. I get so far, I write a stanza, and then I stop. No matter what I do, or how long I work and wait for the inspiration to drive me on, I cannot continue. Yes, most of the initial ideas are mine, but Adèle not only unblocks my valves, she adds something inimitable of her own.

Issy van Randwyck has slipped into the writing with ease. She describes herself as the interior decorator of the team. So if I'm Richard Rogers, and Adèle is Lord McAlpine, Issy must be David Hicks. She sits there, free associating, jotting things down, suggesting, rhyming, making lists, and acting as a catalyst between Her Imperial Glumness (Adèle) and Her Grumpy Distractedness (Me). She is a great encourager, and not afraid to say, 'It's not good enough,' or 'It's not funny enough.' And she's usually right.

The final arbiter is our director, Nica Burns. She's the hardest audience in the world. She makes the Glasgow Empire seem like a pushover. If she hums and haahs, puts her head in her hands, screws up her face, chews cheese, sighs a lot, dictates a letter to Sir Andrew Lloyd Webber, takes a telephone call from Peter Brook and sends a fax to Boutros Boutros-Ghali, the message is that we should go home and prepare a lethal injection for self-administration.

If she sits there stony-faced, humming and haahing, and letting out the occasional bark where we didn't think we'd get a laugh, we know it's okay.

*****

It's a very strange feeling, to look at your songs in print. They look so official, as though someone else wrote them and you had nothing to do with them. It must be a bit like sending a child off in school uniform for the first time. You feel so responsible and at once so incompetent.

I am sad to think this book will never be seen by my best friend, Amanda Walker, who died on 6th May 1988. She wheedled, goaded, bullied, persuaded and begged me to play and write. She sat by the record player for hours upon end, holding the needle above the vinyl, playing phrases over and over again, so that

I could learn them by ear when the music wasn't available or affordable. She advised me, helped me, introduced me to anyone and everyone who could help me, got Fascinating Aïda on air for the first time (on Capital Radio), lent me money to buy an electric piano for an important gig, and sorted out initial problems with the press. And she laughed at my jokes and endured my faulty friendship for sixteen and a half years.

This book is dedicated to her memory, to her very beloved daughter Jessica (my God-daughter) and to all small girls with ill-fitting dreams.

Hello world, it's us!

I LIKE ME

How did this picture of Issy get here? It was supposed to be ME!

The eighties were the Me Decade. Then the nineties were ushered in as the Caring, Sharing Decade. This was a worry. When a whole society has been given the green light to be exclusively concerned with the self, the id, and the ego, and when our voyage into self-discovery and self-knowledge is only just begun, it's a bit of a damper to be told you must care about, and share with, others.

Apart from the sheer distraction of having to pretend you give a toss about the next man, there rose the alarming prospect that one might have to give to a charity without going to a ball. Things got so bad, there was talk that a Save the Charity Ball Ball was being planned.

All these fears proved groundless, happily. The caring and sharing spotlight, however, has not so much been switched off, as had its focus changed. Caring and sharing is still IN, therefore, but the caring and sharing is entirely with oneself. Self-obsession is hip. You only have to look at icons like Barbra Streis and to know that self-obsession pays dividends. Why, Barbra paid hundreds of thousands of dollars to be able to share her wonderful self with us wonderful people, and thereby told us that it was all right to be self-obsessed. Princess Diana withdrew her compassionate self from the public eye, and went off in search of a private life and colonic irrigation. Her husband went in search of sewage. Much the same thing, really. Billy Connolly has given up drink, shaved, and become best friends with Fergie. Anything is possible when one cares about, and shares so passionately with, oneself.

This all is fine by me. There's nothing I like better than caring about me and sharing with me. We get along just swell.

In this song, we all get a chance to say how much we love ourselves. I sing the first verse and chorus — well, actually, I'd sing the whole thing solo given half a chance, but it wouldn't leave me looking very good and, naturally, I am concerned with my image. Issy sings chorus two, Adèle chorus three. Then we all sing a chorus about how much we like each other. This is pure fiction. We loathe one another quite unconditionally. Our dressing room is like the Crimea with cosmetics.

What the hell, have a nice sing.

I LIKE ME

Dillie:

I was feeling dejected, downcast and depressed;
The world was my clam shell, I'd run out of zest;
All alone with no-one to care.
The people I worked with were all self-obsessed,
And beneath the façade, tho' you'd never have guessed,
I was poised on the brink of despair.
Then out of the blue, it all fell into place;
The answer was staring me right in the face ...!

I like me!
I like the me that I see when I'm brushing my teeth in the morning;
I like me!
I find we always agree – it's the others who set us off yawning!
Who is the sweetest, completest companion by far?
Moi!
Who do I long to be with more than *justement un peu*?
Je!
I like me!
When I put my hand on my knee
I don't mind –
I'm my kind!
And I find ev'ry day
I'm enchanted to say
I like me!

Issy:

I like I!
I spy with my little eye the yummiest, scrummiest popsie;
Don't ask why:
I'm my pie in the sky and it's always myself who's on topsie;
When I soap me down in the bath who else dares go that far?
Voilà!
I'm putty in somebody's mitts, what more can I say?
Olé!
I'm so fab!
I'm the absolute dab,
And I'm lush;
Makes me blush;
When I rush to my side
For a jolly good ride
I like I.

Note: We reserve the right to rewrite this song entirely should we ever fall out of love with ourselves.

Adèle:

One loves One!
One is a bundle of fun, when I chase myself, I always catch me!
'Scuse the pun;
But it's simply so wonderful knowing no other can match me:
When life demands answers, then who is most likely to know?
Yo!
When fate bowls a googly, then who is an absolute brick?
Ich!
Je m'adore!
If you saw my *rapport*
You'd cry gee!
Yes, siree!
I'd shag me if I could,
Oh God, I'd be good –
One loves One.

All:

We like we!
We are the three thoroughly nicest people that we've ever been with.
Here's the key!
We never charge us a fee when we're booking ourselves to be seen with.
Who are the ones who will always be faithful and true?
C'est nous!
Whose are the eyes who'd be weeping if we ever got cross?
Nosotros!
We worship we!
We suit us down to a tee –
It's a plus
To be us!
And it's possibly due
To the fact we're not you,
No, we're we!
So *tant pis!*

    Nothing's ever our fault
    'Cause we've all done *Gestalt*,
    C'est jolie being we!
        Oh we know we're the best,
        And it's all thanks to EST
        That we're free to be we!

        Radiant, seraphic,
        Stopping all the traffic,
        That's we! That's we!
        Iridescent, grandiose,
        Loveliness in pantyhose,
        We!

A nightmare for every mother of sons.

I Like Me

Lyrics by Dillie Keane and Adèle Anderson

Music by Dillie Keane

Note: Adèle and I each sing our verses in the key of F (a fifth below the given key of C).
Since female baritones are thin on the ground, however, I've only written it out in Issy's key.

S. I: we! That's we! Ir - id - es - cent, gran - di - ose, love - li - ness in pan - ty - hose, we!

S. II: we! That's we! Ir - id - es - cent, gran - di - ose, love - li - ness in pan - ty - hose, we!

A.: we! That's we! Ir - id - es - cent, gran - di - ose, love - li - ness in pan - ty - hose, we!

Adèle rifles Issy's handbag while Dillie keeps her distracted.

NEW MAN

No-one can quite agree on how this song got written. Its origins seem to be lost in the mists of Adèle's filing cabinet. As far as we can ascertain, it began life as a different song entirely.

You see, there was this other song which had been hanging around for ages called 'Where is He?' As the title suggests, it's about the search for the ideal man, as if there were such a thing. Stupid idea.

In spite of several noble attempts, we have never been able to get 'Where is He?' right. Marilyn and I started it in 1983. We had been commissioned to write a ditty for Valentine's Day for early-morning telly (it was in the days when we'd do almost anything, no matter how tacky, so long as they paid us) and it was a big number for solo soprano with a great Broadway-style tune. Sadly, the lyrics were absolute garbage – romantic, mushy and naff, actually. Just to give you a taster of the tosh level, here's a couplet from the song:

> I'll be his, and still be independent;
> He's the one to make my life resplendent.

Horrible, horrible, oh horrible. The thought of anyone coming along and making my life resplendent is, quite frankly, enough to make me want to turn the lights out permanently.

But I do hate to waste a good tune, and so Adèle and I regularly attempt to rewrite it, excising the horrid slushy 'lurve' bits and injecting it with our particularly beastly brand of cynicism. Each time, we improve the lyrics a little, but not enough. In 1986, we spent two full days trying to rewrite it. We wrestled spectacularly with it, but it's one of those songs that grows heads. We got to the end of two days' work, patted ourselves on the back, sang it through, and realised it was still a turkey. Eventually, we went to the pub in disgust, where over three pints we knocked up a number known as 'Viennese' ('Love's a sham, love's a shit,/But I don't care a bit/For I love to be in love....') which Denise Wharmby sang spectacularly well for two and a half years. So at least we got something for our efforts.

'Where is He?' continues to elude us. We try to improve it, adding counter-point and all sorts of desperate strategies, but it still finds us out and sounds stupid. The last time we tried to rewrite it was in Pudsey, a suburb of Leeds. (And why not? The air in Pudsey is as inspiring as anywhere else.) I need hardly tell you that the efforts were wasted.

Except that Adèle, who is one of Nature's librarians, kept the notes. We had decided to incorporate some ideas about New Men in the song, having discussed exhaustively the sad case of TS and WS (names remain secret to protect the guilty from suing me for libel).

TS is our dear friend: a gentler, more honest woman you would be hard put to find on the planet. WS was her boyfriend, and a more loathsome snake never crawled the earth, save for most of the blokes that we've been out with.

WS was the ultimate New Man. He cooked, cleaned, shopped (with her money), joined a men's group, gave in to tears easily, bonded with other men, bonded with anyone who cared to bond, was spectacularly nice to kids, went on voyages of self-discovery, did holistic massage and various forms of therapy. You name it, he was into it. Mr New Age. If he had had *'I AM A WONDERFUL AND CARING HUMAN BEING'* tattooed on his bottom, it wouldn't have surprised me in the least.

It surprised our poor friend TS, however, when she discovered that he was taking his bonding further than she had realised. Yes, predictably, he was having an affair. And it surprised us all when it was revealed that he had asked his men's group for permission to have his affair – he said TS was 'cramping him' – and they gave him their blessing, bless their smelly football socks.

Anyhow, we had this idea that 'Where is He?' might be improved if we incorporated some digs at New Men, based on the git WS. I remember jotting some ideas down.

Then there's a lacuna. Focus yourself, if you will, on my fevered brain in the last stages of rehearsal before we open our new show at the Lyric Theatre, Hammersmith, in March 1994. We have just done a public run-through in front of some students and I realise we are a song short at the beginning of the show. Panic! I say to Adèle, 'Where are the notes for New Man?'

And the next day, she walks in with the first section completely written. She claims I did most of it in Pudsey. I claim she did it that night. Anyhow, it took about two hours to finish, and seems to work well.

'Where is He?' is still in the file marked Work in Progress.

We dedicate this song to WS. As the Chinese say, may he live in interesting times.

NEW MAN

I

Deep in the heart of the forest
Ev'ry other weekend
The male of the species congregates,
Trying to comprehend;
He goes to reclaim his manhood,
With his inner self commune,
Forge a bond with his fellow man
By pretending to be a baboon.

He bangs his drum;
He beats his chest;
He's very butch;
He removes his vest;
And then he cries,
Just like Tarzan:
'Me Big Feller,
Me New Man.'

New Man, there's no limit if
New Man wants to go primitive,
Holler and hug and have a good blub;
Then off for a bevvy down the pub.

II

Deep in the heart of the kitchen
Women are getting annoyed;
The male of the species wields his wok
And pretends to be Keith Floyd;
From ciabatta to chapatis,
From curly kale to curry;
Dinner will be delicious
So long as you're not in a hurry.

He serves up kumquats
He buys at Waitrose;
He takes no notice
If you say 'I hate those;'
And as he uses
Ev'ry pan
Cries: 'Me Big Chef,
Me New Man.'

New Man wants to use a
New pan by Le Creuset;
He thinks he deserves a cup,
But you're still left with the washing up.

III

Deep in the heart of the bedroom
At the top of the stairs
The male of the species bares his soul
And confesses his affairs;
He says that he has to have them
To fully explore his psyche;
He's hurt and slightly bewildered
When you say: 'Me no likee.'

He'll understand
If you get grumpy;
'Cause what he wants
Is rumpy pumpy;
He'll reassure you
That's not his plan,
Cry: 'Me Big Dyke,
Me New Man.'

New Man, sensitive, sharing,
New Man, considerate, caring;
He'll hold back however long you take,
But he still can't tell if and when you fake.

IV

Deep in the heart of the nurs'ry
Hear the baby weep;
The male of the species lies next door,
Blissfully asleep.

Spoken:

Wake up, you bastard!

New Man

Lyrics by Dillie Keane

Music by Dillie Keane

In modo gagliardo; con ingiustificata mascolinita

Deep in the heart of the for - est ev - 'ry oth - er week - end the
male of the spe - cies con - gre - gates, try - ing to com - pre - hend; He goes to re - claim his
man - hood, with his in - ner self com - mune, forge a bond with his fel - low man by pre -
tend - ing to be a ba - boon. He bangs his drum; he beats his chest; he's

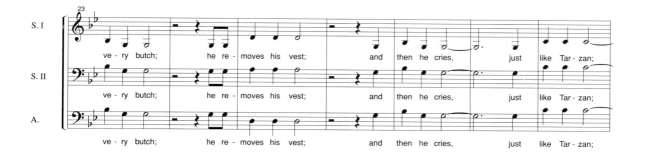

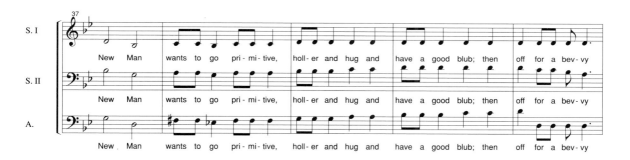

Use modulation to sing each verse 1/2 step up.

Note: This transposes up a semi-tone for each new verse.

Blissfully asleep.
Or what New Man does
when baby sets up a-yowling.

The choreography here is inspired by the Haka, the Maori war dance performed
by the All-Blacks.

THE MAGAZINE SONG

Adèle speaks:

For the shows we did from 1984 until 1989, although I wrote many lyrics, I only ever collaborated on two tunes. One was for a song called 'Rain', and the other was for 'Goodbye and Go', featured later in this book.

In 1991, however, I wrote a one-woman show for the Edinburgh Festival and discovered, to my delight, that I could pen an air or two. My tunes tend towards the jazz idiom, and I twist time signatures to suit myself, but they'd never even see the light of day if someone else didn't transcribe and score them. Recently, it's been the Australian composer, Warren Wills, but in 1991, it was the marvellous Sarah Travis who has worked extensively with Dillie on her one-woman shows.

Sarah and I collaborated on my show, and since then have both written regularly for the Mercury Workshop, a collective whose aim is to get the work of budding composers and lyricists heard and seen. I've appeared in Sarah's musical, Tales My Lover Told Me, *and she was the composer and Musical Director for the two pantomimes I directed at Chipping Norton Theatre. She is a very special friend.*

'The Magazine Song' was written for that Edinburgh show, but most of its lyrics have been substantially rewritten since then. It was the inimitable Miss Keane who suggested making the last magazine Horse and Hound. *She has a great talent for hitting the audience with a sidewinder just when they think they've got a handle on what's going on.*

As Dillie has said in the introduction, I hate rewrites, and I pulled many a long face at our rehearsals in Devon each time she sent me back to my room to have yet another crack at it, exhorting me to 'come up with something better'. (Of course, I'm glad now that she did.) But I got my revenge; Dillie swears it's the most impossible song she's ever had to play in public.

And back to Dillie again:

I could never have dreamt up this baby. I first heard Adèle sing it in Edinburgh, and was thunderstruck by its fiendish construction; note the odd placing of the rhymes, the assonance at the start of each line ('*Diet*', '*Di* was plump', Or *die* each time' ... etc.) and the strange unmatching lengths of the lines. But somehow, it hangs together marvellously, though none of the chords do anything my fingers want to do, and as for that extra half bar, well, strike me pink and call me sailor, it's a bloody monster.

Yes, I made Adèle rewrite it, though, 'cause I'm a horrid bossy boots. Long faces? She looked like the Pardoner in the *Canterbury Tales*. I think she nearly throttled me when I sent her back to her room for the nineteenth time. And then I had a dreadful job learning it, and Her Maj. (Dame Adèle) kept correcting me every single blasted time that we ran through it and I wanted to KILL her.

That's showbiz.

THE MAGAZINE SONG

Dillie:

The bath was run, the candles glowed, I poured out some Château Lafitte;
Pulled a plastic bag over my head – I was giving myself a treat;
I put on some Harry Connick, and also the answer-phone;
Popped a Belgian truffle into me gob, and opened my *Woman's Own*;
And this is what it said ... I read:

You really ought to
Diet;
Di was plump when she married Charles but look how thin she's become;
Diet;
Or die each time you look in a mirror at your lumpy bum;
Diets are tough,
Diets are hard,
But diets are there to help you
Change from looking like a big tub of lard
Who people think resembles Bernard Manning's mum;
Revitalise your make-up;
Make up your mind to use a good blusher that'll flatter you,
Make-up;
Maybe a new hairdo for the no-longer-fatter you;
Wake up and vow
To take up a sport;
Forsake that old look and replace it with
All the swanky frocks that you've bought
And men you meet'll think you're only twenty-two (?!)

Adèle reaches out for her G-spot.

Adèle:

I was walking through the town one day, when suddenly I bumped
Into a handsome Lothario by whom I'd been callously dumped;
I fled home in an awful state and wept through several boxes of tissues;
Then turned for advice to the latest of *Cosmopolitan*'s issues;
And this is what it said ... I read:

You've got to learn to
Orgasm,
Or you'll never know what you've been missing till it's far too late;
Orgasm;
Organic'lly designed to guarantee you'll feel really great;
Orgasms are swell;
Orgasms are fun;
Orgasms are such that ev'ry
Girl ought to know how to have at least
One, two, three, four, five, six, seven, EIGHT!

You've got to find your
G-spot,
Geographic'lly it's inside somewhere rather hard to reach;
G-spot;
Jeepers creepers, you can flex it on the bus or even on the beach;
G-spots are a joy,
G-spots are a GEE!
G-spot manipulation should go hand in
Hand with a nice fantasy
About Tom Cruise or even Stacy Keach (?!)

Issy:

I got home from another opening, the umpteenth night in a row I'd been out;
But as I unzipped my Vivienne Westwood, I was suddenly plagued with doubt;
It seemed such a pointless existence, being constantly wined and dined;
So in order to learn the true meaning of life, I bought a copy of *Horse and Hound*;
And this is what it said ... I read:

You've got to buy a
Hairband;
Hair lair! Haven't seen you for absolutely yonkeroos;
Hairband;
Hare off down to Knightsbridge and get yourself some Gucci shoes;
Hairbands have class;
Harrods have heaps;
A hairband ensures you're accepted by toffee-nosed gits
Who drive around in jeeps
And think that you're a frightful leftie if you refuse
To come and kill some wildlife;
Wipe out half of Gloucestershire with both barrels of your gun,
Wildlife;
Why not pot a shot at a stag when it's on the run;
Wildlife abounds;
So wise up! Wear furs!
And while away each Saturday
By beating up some hunt saboteurs
Who turn up in kagoules and try to spoil your fun.

All:

Well, the three of us got together,
As we're wont to do once in a while;
And put all our magazines together
In an orderly pile;
Then we dropped them off for recycling,
Went home with Chinese food;
Cracked a bottle of tequila,
Got completely smasherooed.

THE MAGAZINE SONG

Lyrics by Adèle Anderson

Music by Adèle Anderson and Sarah Travis

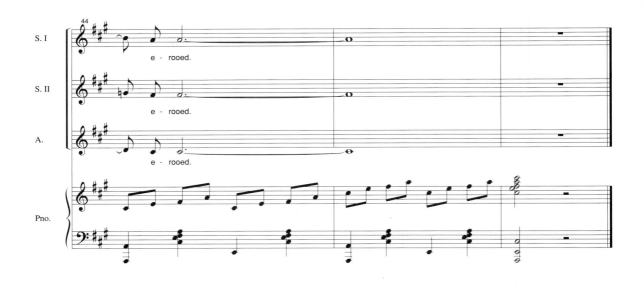

My hat, what gorgeous girls!

KISS AND TELL

Issy speaks:
This was an extremely auspicious and momentous occasion for me: the first Fascinating Aïda song, since I joined the group, that I had been involved with from its creation. We'd been skimming through the papers, desperate for ideas, when a headline hit us right between the eyes, and then another, and another and another – God, this writing process is a painful one – 'Middle-aged politician embroiled in sex romp'; 'Red-faced TV personality caught with pants down'; 'Society lady in hygiene scandal'. Well, not quite, but near enough. 'Kiss and Tell' was conceived. Dillie got out her rhyming dictionary, and started talking about male and female rhymes (not very PC), Adèle had her finger on the grammar (terrifically uncomfortable) and I made the tea and baked some Kup Kakes.

Sensational journalists have been around for ages; take Dillie, for instance. (Please somebody take her.) Recently, however, there's been a new slant on exposés of this type. Ten years ago, tabloid journalists were considered a lower form of life for exposing the extracurricular activities of the famous and not-so-famous, but now people are only too ready to sell their own stories to the highest bidder. It's curious, then, to see how distressed they become when others are reticent to share their soapy water after they've washed their dirty linen in public.

But who are we to question? Fascinating Aïda, that's who!

And back to Dillie again:
I've had an obsession with this subject for a long time. In 1984, Marilyn Cutts and I wrote a song called 'Chequebook Journalism' – we wrote it postally, incidentally; Marilyn was at a health farm and kept sending me pithy little verses and couplets scribbled on the back of diet sheets and work-out programmes. I think she was trying to give me a hint as well as write a song. My profound disregard for the state of my health, and my rock 'n' roll attitude to partying, leave her faint with horror.

Anyhow, 'Chequebook' was a song that took no prisoners. The Press were definitely painted as the demons, bastards who would stoop at nothing to get a story. It was written in the Brecht/Weill style, but with counterpointing tunes à la Irving Berlin. Very flash. A little worthy, looking back, but one of the few songs I've written that I can bear to hear again.

We also sang another song called 'Paparazzi' which was as obvious as its title. It had all the subtlety of Gorgonzola, and I hated singing it almost as much as playing it. Playing it, now that was really ghastly. For some reason, I wrote it in B Minor. I cannot imagine what possessed me. I cannot play in B Minor. It's not a key with which I have any affinity and it was digital torture nightly. The song is best forgotten.

I don't know whether I've changed my mind about the Press, or whether the relationship between Press and punter has changed in ten years, or even whether

I have compromised my stance since working for the *Mail on Sunday*. All three, probably – but it seemed the subject was worth readdressing, and a new approach should be made. The result is a simpler construction than 'Chequebook', but the oleaginous little waltz tune (in A flat – the richest, purplest, loveliest key) is harder to learn than it seems. It slips off the staves and slithers onto the accidentals in a sneaky sort of way. And the lyrics, I hope, implicate everyone and no-one.

After all, no-one would ever kiss and sell if we didn't all buy the newspapers.

KISS AND TELL

All:
Kiss and tell;
Kiss and tell;
Oh we've all got a story to sell;
Don't hold back,
Give him flak;
The best form of defence is attack;
Remember the British obsession with sex,
And tell us how big were his muscular pecs;
Describe how you throbbed as he pulled off his kecks ...
Kiss and tell ... Kiss and tell.
Lovers come; lovers go;
And we feel that the nation should know;
Lovers go; lovers come;
And you'll never get rich keeping mum;
Where d'ya meet? Where d'ya go? Was it love at first sight?
Were you friends with his wife? Was it five times a night?
Did you happen to get that black eye in a fight?
Kiss and tell;
Kiss and tell.

Issy:
I was working as his new researcher/PA;
And his 'bring back the birch' bill was thrown out that day;
He'd been up half the night at the chief whip's behest;
And his wife was up north, he was tired and depressed.
So we went out for dinner – Italian, I think,
And he then asked me back to his flat for a drink;
The poor man was lonely, he wanted a cuddle;
And this is our daughter – oh God, what a muddle....

All:
Kiss and tell;
Kiss and tell;
How you made him fall under your spell;
Was he stripped
While you whipped
In your basement done out like a crypt?

Did he sit in the corner, snort coke and just look?
And is that where he hung upside-down from a hook?
Can you show us the names in your little black book?
Kiss and tell ... Kiss and tell.
Take the cash with panache;
It'll soften the public backlash;
Up the price; add some spice,
Let us into your hotbed of vice;
Was the Major a client? Could you be more forthcoming?
Did he sing 'Rule Britannia' while fondling his plumbing?
Is this the courgette that you used kinky bumming?
Kiss and tell;
Kiss and tell.

Adèle:
We were sharing a house, her room was upstairs;
We were very close friends, we'd discuss our affairs;
Well, I come home one night, they were on the settee,
And I knew who he was from his show on TV;
I know that to him she's just some bit of skirt,
And I'm telling you now 'cause I don't want her hurt;
They were at it all night; they sure had the hots;
Here's the recording and here are the shots ...

All:
Kiss and tell;
Kiss and tell:
Having scruples is all very well;
Just sign here;
Look sincere,
And it might boost your flagging career;
We're publishing anyhow, why be discreet?
We'll stress the bulimia, it goes down a treat;
And we'll use all the ones of him sucking your feet;
Kiss and tell ... Kiss and tell.
Feel no shame – stake your claim
To your own fifteen minutes of fame;
Set your sights on the heights –
Let your publicist handle the rights;
When you kissed in a nightie that showed off your shape,
Did you pass out from drink? Did he bar your escape?
Was it one week or two till you claimed it was rape?
Kiss and tell ... Kiss and tell.
So what if revenge comes across as sour grapes?
The readers will love all those upper-class japes;
And we'll set up a phone line so they'll all hear the tapes;
Kiss and tell;
Kill and tell.

Issy decides on her price.

KISS AND TELL

Lyrics by Dillie Keane, Adèle Anderson and Issy van Randwyck

Music by Dillie Keane

POLITICALLY CORRECT

Big Sisters!

This is quite a cross song. I said to Adèle and Nica that Fascinating Aïda couldn't come back without a song about political correctness, and here it is. Political correctness makes me boil with rage – I consider it to be a very great evil, a creeping fascism, an Orwellian Newspeak designed to censor speech and, ultimately, thought. It is practised by didacts who seek to induce guilt in others. How's that for pomposity? Still, it's how I feel.

There are those who think it's an easy target. Well, all I can say to that is, it's a very big target, but it ain't easy. It's like a canker, it grows all the time. As we wrote, the subject itself kept mutating like a virus; we were the baffled doctors rushing around trying to contain it, but with verse and lyric rather than with medicine.

The result was eighteen months' hard labour. If one of the major problems was getting some jokes in, another was getting the lingo to fit into the lines. As in many cults, not only is the terminology ponderously and deliberately baffling, but the terminology is all. You try finding a rhyme for 'physically challenged'. After writing and hacking, however, chopping and rewriting, weeping and gnashing, we culled something together. I am moderately pleased with it, as I think we've been a little braver than usual. It still isn't finished, though.

We perform it with Nazi salutes and goose-stepping in the last verse. The Nazi salute is the most potent gesture of fascism around, and shows precisely what we think of PC.

POLITICALLY CORRECT

All:
For far too long, we've all been stuck in ancient ways of thinking,
But now we know that language can oppress;
Herstory has shown that while the lads were all out drinking,
Women stuck at home had no redress.
But now those days are over of polish, soap and starch;
The monstrous regiment of women is on the march;
By the chains that held our mothers, we're unencumbered,
So hang on to your hats, boys; your days are numbered....

> 'Cause we're politic'lly correct,
> Yes we're politic'lly correct,
> All phallocentric language we reject;
> With righteous fervour glist'ning,
> Each categ'ry rechrist'ning;
> So watch your language, brothers, big sister is list'ning!
> Men must give in:
> You know you cannot win;
> It's no use agreeing,
> You offend us just by being;
> So though it may seem novel,
> We love it when you grovel;
> That's the way to be politic'lly correct.

Now some men, we admit, are held by ties that bind;
By accident of birth, they have no pow'rs;
Like they're physically challenged, or Greekly inclined,
Or their skin has more melanin than ours.
It's only you Caucasian men who need to be improved,
For we know beneath your trousers, your feet are cloven hooved;
Oh, simply by existing you must be oppressing someone;
If you're white and straight and fit, fate has dealt you a bum one;

> 'Cause we're politic'lly correct,
> Yes we're politic'lly correct,
> So don't use terms to which we might object:
> *Adèle:* If you've lost your legs, sing merrily;
> *Issy:* You're not crippled necessarily,
> *Adèle:* We say you're handicapable
> *Issy:* Or privileged sedentarily;
> *Dillie:* Your hearing's gone;
> You feel you can't go on;
> *Issy:* Don't be negatively labelled;
> *Adèle:* Be silently enabled;
> *All:* If you find all this a trial,
> You're doubtless in denial,
> Relax, and be politic'lly correct.

'Cause we're politic'lly correct,
Yes we're politic'lly correct,
Reclaiming ethnic people's self-respect;
Balzac, Burns and Behan
We're told are European;
But if you really delve I think you'll find
    they're Caribbean;
And it's true
Jane Austen was a Sioux;
Beethoven and Débussy
Were clearly both Watusi;
So show that you're right on
And ban Enid Blyton;
And you can be politic'lly correct.

'Cause we're politic'lly correct,
Yes we're politic'lly correct;
With centuries of wrongs to resurrect;
Issy: Once you've got your man and kicked him,
Adèle: And positively licked him,
Dillie: Only then can you attain the status of a victim;
Adèle: If he starts complaining
Give him sensitivity training;
Dillie: They used the same solution
For the Cultural Revolution;
Issy: It's a wonderful tradition
From the Spanish Inquisition
Who were first to be politic'lly correct.

All:
'Cause we're politic'lly correct,
Yes we're politic'lly correct,
We bow to each minority and sect;
We therefore think it best
That the balance is redressed,
But only we know who's oppressing
    whom and who's oppressed;
So just suppose
Your gran turns up her toes;
She's not dead, we'll be insisting
She's diff'rently existing;
And if you're confused,
Then you must have been abused,
That's okay, 'cause it's politic'lly
    correct.

So change the way that you speak,
And learn to speak in Newspeak,
And you will be politic'lly,
Examine language critic'lly,
Yes you will be politic'lly correct.

THE STORY OF ADAM AND EVE

Once upon a time, a very long time ago, in fact, so long ago that it was at the very beginning of the world, there was a beautiful Garden. And it was called the Garden of Eden.

And two lucky people lived all alone in the beautiful garden, and they were lesbians. We know they were lesbians, because their names were Eve and A Dam. Well, we don't know what A Dam was actually called, but we do know she was a dam.

Anyhow, Eve and A Dam loved their garden, and they looked after all the trees and shrubs and plants and flowers that grew there. And their favourite thing of all was a great big Apple Tree that grew in the centre of the garden, and it gave the most wonderful, crisp, juicy, sweet apples.

Unfortunately, living in the apple tree was the horrible Trouser Snake. He was a wicked fellow, the trouser snake, and he lured Eve and A Dam to the tree. And there he gave them the Recipe for Apple Pie, and they were enslaved in the kitchen from that moment on.

Wasn't that sad, girls and girls?

POLITICALLY CORRECT

Lyrics by Dillie Keane and Adèle Anderson

Music by Dillie Keane

Auntie Dillie's Recipe for Apple Pie: First, take your Asda trolley and head for the ready-made desserts section. Keep an eye out for the name Mr Kipling. The patisserie counter can be helpful too.

Small Talking, Haunted and The Blues Got a Skeleton Key

I have to work with these two.
No wonder I get the blues.

Three Sad Songs

These songs get sadder and sadder, like life. I've had my share of beer and skittles, bowls of cherries and whatnot: ageing party animal, that's me, but these are the bad-time songs.

You think I'm going to explain them? Eat your heart out. Look for clues. it's all there, my life in these songs. I'd like to think I'm always as sour and sanguine as the voice in 'Small Talking'. Most of the time, it works. But sometimes I'm haunted by demons I can't chase, and then the blues creep in by the back door.

Have a depressing sing.

SMALL TALKING

Remember when we used to talk the whole night through?
Now it's just 'Nice to see you,' and 'How are you?'
A chance meeting in a crowded train;
'Well, look who it is! Nice to see you again!'

     Small talking with my old-time lover;
     Small talking with the love of my life;
     Yes, I live with my significant other;
     How's the wife?

The words I want to say won't form in my mouth.
It's just 'How's the new job?' and 'Do you miss the South?'
Distant chit-chat just to pass the time;
Like two old buddies in a pantomime;

     Small talking with my old-time lover;
     Small talking with my old-time pash;
     In case you're asking, yes, I did recover
     From that rash....

     You led the student sit-in;
     I was just trying to fit in;
     Wearing my tie-dye caftan;
     You in your beads and afghan.
     You fanned my youthful fires;
     Took me to hear Joan Baez;
     I loved your air of danger;
     Now you're a boring stranger.

Recall the moment when love turned to dust;
That necklace by the bed that banished trust;
And so it's 'Parents well?' and 'How's the career?'
'Ball-bearings, that sounds fascinating.' Thank God I get out here.

     Small talking with my old-time lover;
     Small talking with my old-time flame
     And by the way, I never did discover –
     What was her name?

     Small talking with my old-time lover;
     Small talking with my old-time mate;
     And don't forget, do give my love to your brother;
     He was great....

Note: There is a discrepancy between the lyrics printed here and those in the music. That's because Adèle keeps trying out new ideas. We thought it best to give you the full choice as it stands at the time of going to press, and reserve the right to sing it completely differently.

SMALL TALKING

Lyrics by Dillie Keane and Adèle Anderson

Music by Dillie Keane

Senza rancore

Re - mem - ber when we used to talk the whole night through?

Now it's just 'Nice to see you,' and 'How are you?'

A chance meet - ing in a crowd - ed train;

HAUNTED

I see you in ev'ry place I go,
When you turn round it's no-one I know;
How could you vanish without a trace,
Leaving your smile on another man's face?
'Cause I'm haunted;
Haunted ...
Haunted.

Trains pull away, was that you I saw?
Then you're there in a revolving door;
Reflected in windows all over town,
In the lift going up I pass you going down;
'Cause I'm haunted;
Haunted ...
Haunted.

Someone has stolen your walk today;
Someone knows just how to talk your way;
I turn around and you're right on cue,
And it's always you and yet it's never you,
'Cause I'm haunted;
Haunted ...
Haunted.

Was that you there at the swimming pool?
Ran to the changing room, what a fool;
Strangers are looking me up and down,
But you are nowhere to be found,
'Cause I'm haunted;
Haunted ...
Haunted.

Pick up the phone, it's your voice I hear;
See you in crowds but you disappear,
Glimpsing your handwriting in the post,
I'm sick of shadows and I'm scared of ghosts,
'Cause I'm haunted;
Haunted ...
Haunted.

When will it cease?
 Leave me in peace,
'Cause I'm haunted;
Haunted ...
Haunted.

Somehow I know,
Wherever I go
I'll be haunted;
Haunted ...
Haunted.

Haunted

Lyrics by Dillie Keane and Adèle Anderson

Music by Dillie Keane

Some-how I know, Wher- ev- er I go I'll be

haunt- ed; haunt- ed... haunt- ed.

haunt- ed; haunt- ed... haunt- ed.

Repeat and Fade

Repeat and Fade

Repeat and Fade

She looks more than just 'molto adulta' in this one.

The Blues Got a
Skeleton Key

You can lock all the doors;
Close up the house;
Pretend you're not home;
Stay quiet as a mouse;
Shut all the shutters and turn out the light;
But the blues got a skeleton key.

You can throw a wild party
For the usual crowd;
Serve margheritas,
Turn the volume up loud;
Burn the candle both ends night after night,
But the blues got a skeleton key.

> Well, the blues don't go with my decor,
> But still they come creepin' in;
> And you can't help wond'rin' what's it all for
> When, without any warnin', your heart hits the floor;
> Bartender, pour me a gin.

You can call up the cops;
File a complaint;
Snort a kilo of charlie;
Live like a saint;
You can hide from your heart and pretend you don't see,
But the blues got a skeleton key.

> Well, the blues don't need any reason
> Just to come up and hit you from behind;
> They'll take you in each and ev'ry season,
> Hold you hostage to each tawdry treason,
> Bartender, pull down the blind.

You can run like the wind,
Or give up the chase;
You can beg them for mercy,
They'll laugh in your face;
'Cause once you're their prisoner, you'll never be free;
Yeah, the blues got a skeleton key.
Yeah, the blues got a skeleton key.

THE BLUES GOT A SKELETON KEY

Lyrics by Dillie Keane and Adèle Anderson

Music by Dillie Keane

Note: *We sing this with lots of oohs and aahs (of the musical variety) in the background but I haven't written them in because a girl's got to keep some things private, for heaven's sake. If you want to work in your own oohs and aahs, however, you're most welcome.*

Not bad for an old girl.

Nica Burns clearly forgot, when she was choreographing this, that I still have to play the piano.

LIEDER

Comic songs usually come much slower than sad songs. Once you've got the idea for a sad song, and a vague shape for the melody, you're away. The ideas for comic songs are harder to find, and then you have the devil of a job cranking them out. Rhyme must be exact, and metre must be rigidly obeyed. Jokes have to be fitted into a certain number of syllables. The God of Absurdity must be a welcome guest. It can be a ghastly process.

At other times, you hit on an idea so complete that the song pops out whole, like the latest baby from a much-used womb. This song was one of those, though it had an odd gestation. In a curious way, I owe it to my ex's manager.

I had been on holiday in the South of France, and was due to meet my ex at Paris airport, as he was flying in from the States. I duly rang his manager, got the time of arrival, caught the train up, made my way to the airport, and waited. And waited.

And waited.

Hundreds of people came off flight after flight, none him. Sobbing over the ground staff, I visualised him at the bottom of the Atlantic. He failed to materialise, either in the flesh or as a name on a list. Finally, I rang his manager's office.

'Oh, sorry Dillie!' they chirruped merrily. 'Did we tell you today? Oh dear, no, it's tomorrow! Gosh and golly! Whoops-a-daisy! *Oooh là là! C'est la vie!* Well, you can have a nice day shopping in Paris, can't you?'

Nice day shopping, indeed. I stamped home to our borrowed flat, still weeping, but with relief and rage. With nothing else to do, I started playing through the records in the flat: *The Greatest Hits of Marlene Dietrich*, *Lotte Lenya Sings Kurt Weill*, and *The Songs of Sarah Leander* who, as the sleeve notes informed me, was the biggest cabaret star in Germany in the thirties and forties. (Actually, she was Norwegian, but we'll let that pass.)

Dietrich sang consistently out of tune, Leander sounded as though she had done her vocal training at the bottom of the Grimethorpe Colliery, and Lenya clearly gargled gravel every morning. The idea crept into my bonce that singing out of tune and being German went together. In fact, it probably didn't matter if you did indeed sing out of tune, so long as you were German.

My ex finally arrived. I told him about my idea. He didn't laugh. He thought it was a rotten idea. I was dispirited. We spent two days in Paris, then joined his band on a tour of Belgium and Holland. I had a lot of time on my hands in Holland, thanks to the liberal drug laws there. Well, you try making conversation with a guitarist whose brain has been mashed to bits with Red Leb. So I wrote another song called 'Little Chef', a Scots ballad about the longing one gets, when far awa' from haem, for the warm, cosy wonder of a griddle fry in that excellent chain of roadside restaurants. My ex didn't think that was funny either.

I got home eventually to rehearsal with Adèle, Marilyn and Nica. I sang them what I'd written of 'Little Chef' and they laughed quite a lot. And we finished off the other verses in about an hour and a half.

Emboldened, I confided my idea about Germans and tunelessness to Adèle. Whilst I cannot tell you that she guffawed immoderately, she was mildly amused, and we'd written the first stanza in two minutes flat. Marilyn then heard it, laughed quite a bit, tweaked what we'd written, improved it considerably, and added a couple of ideas. In walked Nica, who heard the first few lines, laughed loudly (a major achievement) and told us to finish it.

Half an hour later, it was completed. An hour after that, it was learned and Nica had given us the most brilliant choreography, a pastiche of the famous Bob Fosse choreography in *Cabaret*.

Along with 'Sew On A Sequin', it has probably been the most popular Fascinating Aïda song ever. My ex loved it. He loved 'Little Chef' too. He had tears in his eyes when he came backstage, and could hardly speak for laughing. He was just a lousy judge of work in progress.

So thank you to his management, for almost giving me a heart attack and for forcing me to spend a miserable, boring and lonely day in Paris with a strange record collection.

I just wish I could have thought it up an easier way.

Oh, if only Adèle would face the music.

I know it's ridiculous, but where else could I have put my stick?

LIEDER

Doesn't matter, if you sing out of tune,
So long as you're German:
Doesn't matter if you can hardly croon,
So long as you're German.
So if you haven't got a note in your head,
Put on a silly accent instead,
And people will stop wishing you were dead –
So long as you're German.

Doesn't matter if the notes are all wrong,
And people are squirmin':
Just make the tune up as you go along –
Pretend you're German.
And if your voice sounds like it's coming through a strainer,
Sing it out of synch, like Marlene:
And soon, you'll be compared to Lotte Lenya,
Who was German.

*Nicht Hinauslehnen Sprechgesang Zauberflöte wunderbar, Johnny
Wiener Schnitzel, Boris Becker, Sturm und Drang, Cooch Behar, Johnny!*

So if you've ever wondered what you have to do
To sound like a Hun:
Just chain smoke from the tender age of two:
That's how it's done.
And when the audiences are all walking out,
Just make believe that you're a Kraut,
Then open your mouth and shout
In German,
In German,
Auf deutsch.
Jawohl.

Lieder

Lyrics by Dillie Keane, Adèle Anderson and Marilyn Cutts

Music (if you can call it that) by Dillie Keane

Con bieca efficienza

Lyrics under the staves:

Does-n't mat-ter if you sing out of tune, so long as you're Ger - man. Does-n't mat-ter if you can hard-ly croon, so long as you're Ger - man. So if you have-n't got a note in your head, put on a sil-ly ac-cent in-stead, and

solo
peo-ple will stop wish-ing you were dead, so long as you're Ger - man. Does - n't

solo
Nicht hin-aus - leh - nen Sprech-ge-sang Zau-ber-flöte wun-der - bar

solo
John - ny! Wie-ner Schnit-zel, Bo-ris Beck-er, Sturm und Drang, Cooch Be-

solo
har John - ny! So if you've shout in

solo
Ger - man, in Ger - man, Auf Deutsche, Ja - wohl!

COLD WAR

Legovia's national symbol is the sickle and knitting needles. This is because all our men are reapists and our women are knits.

The favourite question of journalists is: 'How would you describe Fascinating Aïda?' The favourite answer from me is: 'Um ...'

It seems to cause enormous frustration that there isn't a convenient pigeonhole for Fascinating Aïda. In truth, I myself don't know how to describe what we do, except to say that we run the full gamut of high and low comedy, mainly through song. Perhaps we could be described as sophisticated buffoons.

At the start of Act Two, we have a tradition of getting into character and being very silly whilst disguised as other personae. The critics generally hate it, but we love it. They want us to be sophisticated, mordant and witty all the time. They would like us to inherit the mantle of Noël Coward and Tom Lehrer, and we can't do that if we slip on a banana skin. They wonder why we do it – well, we do it because we can, and because it gets bloody tedious being sophisticated, mordant and witty all the time. And because we admire the Marx Brothers every bit as much as Coward and Lehrer. And because we don't want our audience to be exclusively composed of middle-England, middle-class people with babysitters back home. We want kids and grannies, and rich and poor, and intellectuals and country bumpkins sitting in the audience.

Finally, and probably most importantly, we clown around because I am excellent at falling down. Of all the things I can do, I personally consider that falling down is my greatest skill. Getting a laugh through falling down is the greatest happiness I know, bar playing dressing-up with my nieces. As I trundle into early middle-age, I dare say that my falling-down days are limited, and I shan't be able to do it forever. This causes me great sadness.

Our old alter-egos were the Brontë Sisters, three country-and-western singers on the cusp of madness. Now we are the Trio Bazurka, three generations of singers from a little-known country called Legovia, behind the old Iron Curtain. I am the old babushka, Bulga. Adèle is Mama Olga, and Issy is young Vulga, champion gymnast in search of a husband.

You've never heard of Legovia? This is because it was left off the map after the Treaty of Versailles by decadent Western cartographers. Once it sheltered 'neath the mantle of Mother Russia, but now it is a small, shakily independent country with galloping inflation and a glut of unharvested gherkins. It is sandwiched between the fundamentalist country of Yashmakistan, and the land of Aubergine-baijan, a nation of vegetables. There are many peoples in Legovia, the main ethnic groupings being the Molars, the Dealars, the Burgars and the Slobs. We ourselves are Slobniks, hailing from the lovely city of Harmoniev, which looks across the Whitewater river (a very dangerous stretch of water) at the twin city of Discordiev.

I spent a month behind the old Iron Curtain, and five years listening to Bulgarian folk singing, doing the groundwork that eventually became the Bazurkas. I also did twenty-five years' hard research on the effects of alcohol. I am still researching drinking, and mine's a dry white wine in the bar after the show.

COLD WAR

Bring back the cold war, when life was secure,
The state was our mother, and thinking was pure;
When we went through the year with just one pair of shoes,
And the queues ... ah the queues....
Khruschev was our father, our great benefactor,
And a young man in spring sang love songs to his tractor;
And on the TV it was always good news,
And the booze ... ah, the booze....

Now we must love the Yankees that we once despised;
Ev'rything that we valued has been Westernised;
Thousands of people ask if they can be baptised,
And they say that they believe in God.
Hoy!

None of us worked, though we had full employment,
And informing on friends was a source of enjoyment;
As guests of our allies, our soldiers walked tall;
And the Wall ... ah, the Wall....
State holiday camps in Siberia were fun,
And at the Olympics, the medals we won;
Our women grew beards, they were so big and hearty,
And the Party ... ah, the Party....

Bring back the good times when it was okay if we
Joined something like the Stasi or the KGB;
Now ev'rybody wants to work at KFC
And they say McDonald's is the biz.
Hoy!

Bring back the old days of dogs up in space,
And nuclear missiles, all primed, just in case;
The red flag flew high, and our spirits flew higher;
Stolichnaya ... ah, Stolichnaya....
Our soap was so good, there was only one brand,
And ev'rything fresh was bottled or canned;
Cognac and cabbage, champagne, caviare!
And the Tsar ... ah, the Tsar....

But now, they don't read Pushkin, they read Mills and Boon,
No more Tschaikowsky, all they want is *Brigadoon*,
What's more, the Bolshoi have announced that coming soon,
Sunset Boulevard and also *Cats*.
Hoy!

We'd say as the Hammer and Sickle unfurled,
'Lenin's in his tomb, and all's right with the world;'
Now ev'ryone's singing democracy's song;
What went wrong? What went wrong?
The old days were, oh, so much better because
At least then we knew who our enemy was;
And now where's the vodka production all gone?
Warrington ... Warrington....

Now you see why our country is called Legovia.

COLD WAR

Lyrics by Dillie Keane, Adèle Anderson and Issy van Randwyck

Music by Dillie Keane

Con nostalgia

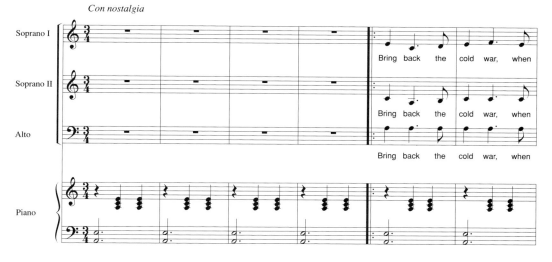

Song Cycle

Ever since the first moment I heard the incandescent, eerie harmonies of Bulgarian folk singing, I had been conceiving a rather grandiose scheme for writing a Bulgarian-style song cycle. I wasn't at all sure what form it would take, or what kind of lyrics it would require, but I often find that inquiring too deeply into my own ideas makes them disappear without trace. If I just let them simmer away in an outhouse of my mind, they have a chance of cooking nicely. So while we were devising the Bazurkas, I assured everyone I'd be providing them with the sheet music written out in my own fair hand in no time. We wrote a few silly clerihews over coffee break, and I took them off home.

Then I tried to make a start, and it was terrifying. I realised that whilst I had listened to a good deal of Bulgarian folk music, I had no real idea how it all worked.

So I started out by basing the first song, 'Insomnia', on an actual Bulgarian folk tune. The middle bit is mine, but I can't claim the main tune. It seemed to work quite well, and so I felt encouraged enough to complete the song cycle. It sounds quite authentic to my ears, and to those few who are familiar with that unique Balkan sound. Mind you, I dread some real Bulgarians hearing it. They'd find me out as a hopeless fake in no time at all.

It is a stinker to sing, but enormous fun once you get the hang of it.

Insomnia

When you lie in bed at night, does it ever trouble you
Knowing Rover has been bought out by BMW?
But the truth is very clear; you were not much fonder
Of Honda.

Fame

Kenneth Branagh
Has a very pleasant manner;
Many of his films are fine,
But let's face it, he ain't Eisenstein.

Finance

Many names at Lloyds are now compelled to live as vagrants;
This is with no thanks to Mary Archer and her fragrance.

Tribute To Lady At Number Ten

Norma,
Hi!
Not a happy performer;
Hi!
How you long to be in some other land
Hearing op'ra stories from Joan Sutherland;
How you must pray to Our Lady of Fatima
That you never heard the name Claire Latimer.

Community

Many people disagree
With what we call the EC;
We hate Brussels bureaucrats,
They're all just a bunch of prats;
Brussels prats;
Hi!
Why do the British ignore the fact that every year the EC becomes more horrible?
It's Delorable.
Brussels prats;
Hi!

Encore

Princess Di is gone and you miss her;
Old Prince Charlie didn't want to kiss her;
He ignored the charms of his bride;
He preferred Camilla Park'n'Ride.

Vulga demonstrates the movement that staggered the judges at the Barcelona Olympics.

Insomnia

Lyrics by Dillie Keane, Adèle Anderson and Issy van Randwyck

Music by Dillie Keane

FAME

Lyrics by Dillie Keane, Adèle Anderson and Issy van Randwyck

Music by Dillie Keane

Con soddisfazione ingiustificata

Soprano I: Ken - neth Bra - nagh

Soprano II: Ken - neth Bra - nagh

Alto: Ken - neth Bra - nagh

S. I: has a ve - ry plea - sant man - ner; Ma - ny of his

S. II: has a ve - ry plea - sant man - ner; Ma - ny of his

A.: has a ve - ry plea - sant man - ner; Ma - ny of his

S. I: films are fine, But let's face it, he ain't Ei - sen - stein.

S. II: films are fine, But let's face it, he ain't Ei - sen - stein.

A.: films are fine, But let's face it, he ain't Ei - sen - stein.

Finance

Lyrics by Dillie Keane, Adèle Anderson and Issy van Randwyck

Music by Dillie Keane

Tribute to Lady at Number Ten

Lyrics by Dillie Keane, Adèle Anderson and Issy van Randwyck

Music by Dillie Keane

COMMUNITY

Lyrics by Dillie Keane, Adèle Anderson and Issy van Randwyck

Music by Dillie Keane

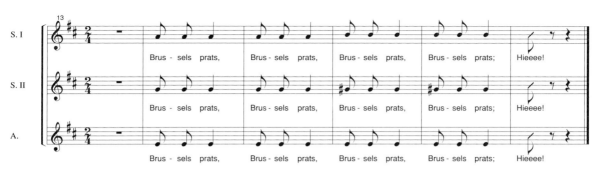

The Trio Bazurka with two elderly relations. Mama Olga dreams of the next Five Year Plan, Babushka Bulga thinks of the last Five Year Plan, and Vulga plans to marry a Westerner and get the hell out.

ENCORE

Lyrics by Dillie Keane, Adèle Anderson and Issy van Randwyck

Music by Dillie Keane

SONG OF GENETIC MUTATION

Never mind genetic mutation: here we make our very own three-headed monster.

This tune had been hanging round for some time. Years back, we'd written a slightly mawkish little numero about seaside holidays – yet another commission. It was almost a good song; the choruses were nice, but the verses were quite frightful.

I've had the air of the chorus ear-marked for a re-tread ever since. As we gradually heard more and more about the horrific reality of genetic mutation, and withered old trouts being artificially inseminated way beyond their menopause, I dusted out the old tune, gave it a new verse, and hey presto, a curiously Catholic song was born. (Scratch my surface and you'll find a collapsed Catholic.)

Then Adèle wrote chorus two, which contains the two best lines in the song. A joyously good lyric, in my estimation.

The reference to the Y-shaped pram is a little homage to Joe Orton.

This song is a shining example of a technique that I learned from Tom Lehrer, the greatest satirical songwriter ever, and I have used it over and over again. The premise is simple: the more unpleasant the lyrics, the more glutinous the tune. Each subverts the other.

In satire, subversion is all.

SONG OF GENETIC MUTATION

Two little pairs of big brown eyes;
Two little button noses;
Two little smiles in two little faces;
Four little cheeks like roses;
Two little fellas born under the crab,
Conceived in a little glass tube in a lab,
Yes, you're a unique scientific creation ...
The very last word in genetic mutation....

Dear little two-headed baby;
Darling wee lamb –
How lucky I am;
Double the brains of an ordin'ry child,
Asleep in a Y-shaped pram;
Two little mittens and two or three boots;
One and a half sets of birthday suits;
Oh what a gift –
But murder to lift –
That two-headed baby of mine.

Dear little two-headed baby;
While you're asleep,
You baa like a sheep;
Though your first steps will be hard to take
For mankind you're a giant leap;
How I'd longed for a child – it was well worth the wait;
What joy to give birth at a hundred and eight;
Christened in church,
All thanks to research,
That two-headed baby of mine.

They ask how I stick it,
Well it's handy for cricket ...
That two-headed baby of mine.

Song of Genetic Mutation

Lyrics by Dillie Keane and Adèle Anderson

Music by Dillie Keane

LET'S GO TO A HOTEL

It is very exciting when you hear a voice that inspires you to song. It is even more thrilling when the owner of that voice consents to sing your ditties.

I first met Issy van Randwyck at my birthday party. She was brung along by my good pal, Victor Lownes. He introduced Issy with the unforgettable words: 'This is Issy van Randwyck. She's a really great cabaret singer. You should have her in your group.'

Since Victor is a man of culture and discernment, and the man who brought the legendary Mabel Mercer to Britain for the first time, I rate his opinion very highly. (In case the name Mabel Mercer means zilch to you, Frank Sinatra says that he learned everything about phrasing from Mabel Mercer. Which is enough for me.)

I stored Victor's words away carefully, and kept my eye on Ms van Randwyck. I had a gypsy feeling that he might be absolutely right.

I didn't actually hear her sing till the moment we asked her if she'd like to come along and have a trial sing-along-at-home. Well, I'd heard her in the distance once, but it was only a few notes across a damp, if noble, lawn. Strangely, those few notes were enough.

I had been booked to do the cabaret at the annual charity cricket match at Blenheim Palace; I was due to do a turn in the celebrity tent. This being Britain, it rained cats, dogs, hens, lemurs: an entire bloody menagerie fell from the sky. I set off anyhow, feeling I ought to show willing. Sure enough, the match was cancelled, but the celebrity was still in the tent (Bill Wyman being the only celebrity in sight), and various hangers-on and ducal retainers were still swinging when I arrived. As I trudged, cursing, across the sodden Blenheim turf, I heard a beautiful voice trilling out of the celebrity tent and into the Oxfordshire air.

As I walked in, Ms Issy had just finished her set. I had missed her performance! Rats! But at least the voice from the marquee had sounded pretty hotsy-totsy to me. I knew in that instant that we had to have her for the group, and the group was suddenly worth re-forming if we could persuade her to join. It was time to impress her.

So I bought raffle tickets. Okay, it doesn't sound too impressive, but I'm lucky with raffles. It started with a bottle of Jaborandi Hair Tonic in the African Leper Colony Raffle when I was twelve, and it's been onwards and upwards ever since. My winnings have included a Tiffany paperweight, a gallon of Martini and twenty pounds of rhubarb (I am still eating the jam). Listen, I am one of life's raffle winners. I still have a free dirty weekend waiting for me at a Norfolk Hotel, if only I could find someone I could be bothered to be dirty with.

So me buying raffle tickets can be a durn sight more impressive than it sounds on paper. And as they began the draw, I said to Issy, over a celebrity scone, 'I'm going to win one of these prizes.' She looked at me as though a rather large pimple had erupted on the side of my nose.

Someone got up to pull the tickets and announce the prizes. 'A day's fishing on the River Tweed. A Barbour jacket from Fab Barbours of Chipping Norton. Dinner for two at the Lochyle Hotel, Shetland.' No, I didn't want those. The tension was plummeting. 'Two tickets to see Harry Connick Jr at the Albert Hall.'

'Yo!' I cried. Most unlike me, I know, but I was in a Yo! sort of mood. 'Yo! This is the one prize I want,' I said to Issy. 'I'll win this.'

And I did.

Naturally, she was tremendously impressed, and I think she got the idea that I could do anything. It was an excellent start.

And here she is now, singing our songs, and writing with us. Hooray!

'Haunted' was written specially for her, and indeed was partly inspired by her – well, I was rather haunted by her since the fateful first meeting. 'Hotel' was penned in Pudsey, a charming suburb of Leeds, and rewritten for Issy when we knew she was joining the group. Her performance of 'Hotel' is so erotically charged that we hear rumours that the hotel business is coming out of recession faster than any other part of the economy.

By the way, Harry Connick Jr was quite brilliant. I took Adèle for her birthday.

Let's Go to a Hotel

Let's go to a hotel;
Let's go to a place where they don't know us well;
Don't keep the receipt,
That's how most wives discover their husbands' deceit.
We'll take all precautions to cover our tracks,
We'll meet in the bar and try to relax,
So let's drown our guilt with a couple of gins,
'Cause this is a game that nobody wins;
Come Sunday, I'll ask God to pardon my sins,
Oh, let's go to a hotel.

Let's fall thru' the door;
Let's rip off our clothing and roll round the floor;
Please, turn down the light;
It's mid-afternoon and we want to pretend that it's night;
God, it's so thrilling to take such a risk;
Do it again, but mind your slipped disc;
You Michael Douglas and me Sharon Stone;
I've seen all the films and I know how to moan;
Yes, that's so good! Don't answer the phone ...
Oh, let's go to a hotel.

There isn't much time for finesse when you're having a quickie;
So don't get too carried away, and give me a hickey;
I'd quite like to see you again, but you're even vaguer;
Please – try not to tear it, it's Janet Reger.

Let's not get involved;
Let's just keep it casual as we first resolved;
Don't ring me at home;
Make sure you remove my blonde hairs from your comb;
Don't mention my name at the office too much;
I earn more than you – I insist we go Dutch;
We're bound to be safe if we stick to the rules,
It'll lessen the pain when the lovemaking cools,
But for now let's behave like two passionate fools,
Oh, let's go to a hotel.

Ev'ryone does it these days, so why should we worry?
It's much more exciting to do it when one has to hurry;
I'm certain your colleagues suspected the moment I met them;
Yes, I did bring the condoms, 'cause somehow you always forget them.

Let's bathe in champagne;
Eat strawb'rries and cream from my navel, it drives me insane;
Quick, let's take a shower;
Remember we've got to be out of here in half an hour;
Get out our diaries – when shall we meet?
Is that your youngest? She looks awfully sweet;
So it's farewell hotel room of orange and brown,
Act casual if we ever meet up in town;
I've got to cook supper – oh God, put me down!
Oh, let's go to a hotel.

Contrary to public opinion, these dresses are perfectly safe. Inside, they're constructed like the Clifton Suspension Bridge.

LET'S GO TO A HOTEL

Lyrics by Dillie Keane and Adèle Anderson

Music by Dillie Keane

BACK WITH YOU

Our songs divide pretty neatly into two categories: the personal and the impersonal.

When it comes to the personal songs, people always want to know how autobiographical they are. The strange fact is that they usually get written entirely from the imagination, but they have this uncanny habit of pre-dating fact. Yes, they keep coming true, and it's extremely sinister.

One such song that springs to mind is one we wrote some years ago, called 'Rain', which came true with alarming speed. The next day, in fact. I had to cancel my barbecue. Actually, there were a couple of lines in that which were remarkably prescient:

> Rain always reminds me of you ...
> Drip, drip, drip....

Another song that came true was a song that I wrote called 'Single Again, and at My Age'. I wrote it at a time when I was halfway through a very long relationship. I didn't, of course, realise that I was halfway through at the time, but as luck would have it, I was. We were going through a period that I think of as an emotional Chernobyl, and I seriously contemplated splitting up, leaving and handing him his pink slip (he was into that sort of thing). Instead, I wrote 'Single Again, and at My Age', which alarmed me so much that I decided against leaving. That took another three and a half years.

Then in 1993, Adèle and I met up on one of our many sessions when we were laboriously attempting to put together a collection of new songs. In Pudsey – Pudsey again! – we wrote 'Back With You'. (We owe a great deal to Pudsey.) When we finished the song, we realised with an awful jolt that we had unwittingly completed the story where 'Single Again, and at My Age' had left off. It was like discovering that you've finished a picture unconsciously.

And all I can say is that if this song predates fact, I'm stuffed.

BACK WITH YOU

Back with you;
Oh, why the hell did I go back with you?
The very thing I swore I'd never do;
What on earth was I thinking?
I must have been drinking.
Lonely nights
Made me forget all those appalling fights,
Ignore the lows and just recall the heights;
Who said true love conquers?
I must have been bonkers!
　　　We were almost happy for a week, and then
　　　Back you went to your old wicked ways again;
　　　Bloody men....
I'm deranged
To kid myself that you had really changed;
I'd like to see your features rearranged;
This is far from an idyll,
In fact it's a riddle,
Why I'm back with you.

　　　It's back to bloody socks that wait for me to pick them up;
　　　It's back to bloody Spurs and how they're doing in the Cup;
　　　It's back to ironing shirts because you're always in a rush;
　　　It's back to hairy plugholes – and would you please just flush!
　　　When anything needs doing, you conveniently vanish;
　　　And those nights when you're late home – oh yes, of course, you're learning
　　　　　Spanish;
　　　You treat me like a little piece of dirt beneath your foot –
　　　Which, if you don't mind me saying – up with which I will not put.

But I make no bones;
I'm just a martyr to my pheromones,
The thrilling way that you explore my zones;
Lost in sensation,
Brain on vacation....
When you're near,
The hurt and anger seem to disappear,
And when you work at it, you sound sincere;
It really is galling –
I just keep on falling....
　　　You think saying sorry takes the pain away;
　　　Then you snap your fingers and assume I'll stay –
　　　Oh, okay....
I'm aware
That we are not a very well-matched pair;
Still I'm the Ginger to your Fred Astaire;
Like a horse to the water,
Or a lamb to the slaughter,
I'm back with you.
I'm always the sucker
And you, you're the ... oh!
Well, I'm just back with you, that's all.

BACK WITH YOU

Lyrics by Dillie Keane and Adèle Anderson

Music by Dillie Keane

SOCIALIST BRITAIN

I don't mind telling you that I sobbed my heart out at the 1992 election. My parents were up staying with me, good Tories both who cannot understand this quisling they've raised, and my evident distress dimmed their joy at another Conservative term. What a gloomy night that was.

The following week, I was asked to write a song for the Radio 4 talk programme, *Stop the Week,* which I had done regularly for nine very pleasant and challenging years. It was one of my very last batch, as it turned out, because the programme was axed that summer. Very sad.

The subject I was given was, as I recall, fantasies and dreams. Adèle and I agreed pretty quickly that a Socialist Britain was a powerful dream we both shared. Issy is not quite so committed, but like us she believes that the people at the bottom of the heap should get a better deal, and so she sings it with gusto, which is sporting of her.

Here's to it.

We hear the news that the Tories have got in again.

SOCIALIST BRITAIN

Over the rainbow somewhere, there's a magical land;
Where everyone's happy all the time, 'cause ev'rything is so grand.
And in ev'ry buttonhole, there's a red rose;
There's no harm in dreaming, I don't suppose....

Socialist Britain,
Socialist Britain,
When shall I see thee again?
Where prescriptions are free
And the late GLC
Is back in the hands of Red Ken.

Socialist Britain,
Socialist Britain,
I hear your Utopian call;
Where there's no cardboard city
And compassion and pity
Are not an excuse for a ball.

Where school books and hospital beds are not axed,
And it isn't the poor, but the rich who are taxed;
Where Cheadle is just as important as Cheam,
And Margaret Thatcher was just a bad dream.

Socialist Britain,
Where folk aren't hard-bitten
From thinking life ain't worth a dime;
Where the government's green,
And the water is clean,
And non-privatised trains run on time.

Where Prince Charles goes to work ev'ry day on the bus;
And the Argies and Germans don't sell coal to us;
Where secret donations don't come from abroad;
And Major is merely a musical chord....

Socialist Britain,
Oh shall it be written
That our striving must all end in tears?
Thou art so far away –
And yet you must stay
Just a dream for another three years.

SOCIALIST BRITAIN

Lyrics by Dillie Keane and Adèle Anderson

Music by Dillie Keane

SEW ON A SEQUIN

The woman who inspired the song.

What can I say about this song? It's terribly silly, in fact it's ridiculous, and yes, it is the campest thing since the last World Convention of Boy Scouts but, apart from 'The Herpes Tango', it's the one song written by me that I love with all my heart. You see, it's completely true. If you've discovered a sheep in your boyfriend's bed, and that job you wanted has been given to Michelle Pfeiffer, and the bailiffs have taken away your Shirley Bassey collection, it's no use sitting sobbing at home, feeling like a piece of half-chewed tripe. There is only one guaranteed cure. Not drink (though that can help). Not drugs (a temporary measure only). Not even a bloody good shag and the loan of an early Iris Williams album.

Sequins. Sequins are the only guaranteed cure for depression that I know. Put on something glittery, throw a bit of Polyfilla over the old visage, totter out in a pair of stilettos and not only will you feel better about yourself, you'll make yourself laugh because you look so daft.

I play this song to myself when horrible things happen, like the Tories win another election, and it always acts like the cooling stream upon the panting hart. Balm to the soul, this song. And balm to the soul, too, to know that there are little Sew On a Sequin Clubs up and down the land, that gay men have had it played at their funerals, and that it means something to quite a few people.

I hope you, too, will find in it some little nugget of truth, some little pearl of wisdom, that you can take away with you and lock into your hearts. For it will help you through the long, dark years ahead.

Sing out, Louise!

SEW ON A SEQUIN

Adèle:
When life has got you down;
You're broke, you're on your uppers,
And you don't know who to call your friend;
When for weeks and months you've roughed it,
And your Pekingese has snuffed it,
And you think you've really reached the bitter end;
When your mother-in-law has run
Away with your teenage son,
And the river, yes, the river's your only hope;
Don't do it – no, don't jump!
Take a tip from me, you chump,
And listen, 'cause here's the only way to cope:

Sew on a sequin, it's sure to cheer you up;
Sew on a sequin when you've drained life's bitter cup;
Sequins will brighten up the oldest shabby dress;
Sequins are guaranteed to bring you happiness.
A sequin is such a little thing
But sure as hell, you know that it'll bring
You through when you've got writer's block;
Yes, it's easier to smile
As you face each fearful trial,
When you've got a bit of heaven on your frock.

Dillie:
You think you've reached rock bottom;
Those low-down blues, you got 'em,
'Cause your fiancé's made some other girl his wife;
You're at the altar, jilted;
The flowers are all wilted,
You're tumbling through the waste-disposal chute of life;

Issy:
Keep your chin up, don't be a funk.
Pack your trousseau in a trunk,
You've no money — then go out and sell the ring;
Paint some lipstick and powder on, please,
And throw away those dungarees,
And go and make some other man your king....

Adèle:
Tack on some tinsel, you owe it to yourself;
Add some diamanté and you'll climb back off the shelf;
Fix on some feathers, ruche some tulle around your hem,
Then you can face the future with the right amount of phlegm.
Ladies, we always must a-
-Tempt to keep our lustre,
For you never know what passion you'll arouse;
So darlings, don't be bitter,
Be lib'ral with the glitter
And embroider lots of moonbeams on your blouse.

All:
Sew on a sequin when you've felt fate's piercing dart;
If you're in the equinox of life, 'twill cheer your heart;
Gather your organza, shimmer, shine, be gay;
Don't give in to tears — just emulate the milky way.
Though a sequin's wee, it twinkles,
Takes the focus off your wrinkles,
For a sequin more is e'er a trouble less;
So ply your needle through that hole,
Or just glue one to your mole,
And strew a spot of stardust,
Ev'ry girl from near and far must,
Strew a spot of stardust on your dress.

If you can't get hold of any sequins, go out and pluck a bird.

Sew on a Sequin

Lyrics by Dillie Keane

Music by Dillie Keane

Written in 1984 © 1987 by Sweet 'n' Sour Songs

GOODBYE AND GO

And lo, an angel appeared before them.

I t's thank-you time now.

1)   Thank you, dear reader, for getting this far. Unless of course you opened it from the back and you're one of those people who always skips to the end, which is CHEATING, so go back to the beginning immediately and read it in THE RIGHT ORDER, and NEVER let me catch you doing that again.

2)   Thank you, dear Adèle, for penning this elegant little number which we always sing if a second encore is required by our marvellous audiences who REFUSE to go

home, BLAST THEM, do they think we have NOTHING better to do than stand there singing all night, to which the answer is NO, we have absolutely NO life whatsoever because all we EVER wanted to do in the first place was stand on stage and sing for a living.

3)   Thank you, dear audience, for behaving like old and beloved friends, for refusing to go away without a second encore, and for making us feel like Sally Field at the Oscars ('You LIKE me! (Sob, sniff.) You really LIKE me!') and for FINALLY getting the message that if we sing ONE MORE BLOODY SONG, we will have absolutely no puff left for the good burghers of wherever we're touring to the following night.

4)   Thanks a second time, dear Adèle, for inspiring 'Sew On A Sequin', and for singing it like an AMAZON all these years.

5)   ... and to ALL members of Fascinating Aïda, in order: Marilyn Cutts, Lizzie Richardson, Glenda Smith and Denise Wharmby and of course the FABULOUS, INSPIRATIONAL, ISSY VAN RANDWYCK, without whom most of these songs would never have been sung, and of course to my INCOMPARABLE friend, ADÈLE ANDERSON, without whom most of these songs would have remained half-written, and the ASTONISHING NICA BURNS, who translates my madness into theatre.

6)   ... belatedly to Miss Morris, Mrs Stonor, Miss Ridgeway, Miss Bethwaite and the magnificent Mrs Friedlander, who had the GRIM job of teaching me pianoforte lessons.

7)   ... to Ma and Pa who had to stump up the shekels for lessons for YEARS, and who BULLIED me into practising in the cold, cold sitting room LONG before we had central heating so that my fingers nearly BROKE OFF, and who hardly ever make me feel bad nowadays for not playing the Grieg piano concerto at the Albert Hall, and to the rest of the family for listening to my AWFUL practising without EVER complaining.

8)   ... to that nice Mr Strachan of Methuen, whose gentle BUT PERSISTENT encouragement since the break-up of Fascinating Aïda in 1989 gave me the will to do it AGAIN.

9)   ... to Rudyard Kipling, for that ridiculous poem, 'If', which has DOGGED my thoughts since I read it so often on the framed copy in Mr and Mrs Murray's loo, and has me trying to fill the unforgiving minute with sixty seconds' worth of distance run every RUDDY minute of the day, not to mention building things with WORN-OUT TOOLS.

10)   ... to fish, for its brain food; to Mars, for their Bars, and to my garden, for solace.

11)   ... to Tom Lehrer, for leading the way, and showing us all how it should be done.

12) ... to Michael Fitzgerald, for being the SOUNDEST sounding board in the whole world.

13) ... to GORGEOUS GEORGE WALLACE, my very good friend who turned up out of the blue just in the nick of time to help on this book. We met in 1984 at the Edinburgh Festival, when he was in the Brass Band, the crazy Californian band who were like all my Christmases come at once. They were up for the Perrier Award, and so were we, amongst others. We said we didn't mind if we didn't win, so long as the Brass Band won. They did. So we gave them the champagne we'd hoped to drink in celebration, and became firm friends. George is a musician, musicologist and performer EXTRAORDINAIRE. We wrote out the music in this book together, but I couldn't have done it at all if he hadn't helped me to understand the BLOODY SOFTWARE on my computer. I mean, I can write out the singing parts myself, but trying to figure out WHAT ON EARTH I play every night was a GHASTLY STRUGGLE. Without you, George, I couldn't have done it. THANK YOU MOST OF ALL.

14) And thank you to Peter Hill, for the very SWANKY Italian translations of my musical instructions. It makes my ditties feel almost like PROPER music.

15) Finally, to Richard Johnson, for turning Fingals Hotel into a HAVEN for writing and rehearsing. A UNIQUE man: a UNIQUE place.

GOODBYE.

Goodbye and Go

Tick tock, tick tock, tick tock ... (etc.)
Your night is drawing to a close
But ours has just begun.
You're off to seek some sweet repose,
We're out to have some fun;
Our dressing room is thronged with beaux
Whose manly hearts we've won;
They'll take us where the champagne flows
Until the morning sun.

So,
Why don't you go
Then we can go
Out where we go ev'ry night.

We've done our stuff,
It must be enough;
Why make yourselves suffer, all right?

You have been so inspiring,
But singing all night is so damn tiring,
And what is more, we are all
perspiring.

So
Into the show'rs
Or in a few hours,
Just like our flow'rs
We will die.

Boy, are we spent!
It's time we went.
So ladies and gents,
Goodbye!
 Goodbye!
  Goodbye!
   GOODBYE!!

GOODBYE AND GO

Lyrics by Adèle Anderson

Music by Adèle Anderson and Dillie Keane

Con un' occhiata di straforo all' orologio

That's all, folks!